SESAME STREET®

Let's Help!

written by Lori C. Froeb

studio **fun** BOOKS

White Plains, New York • Montréal, Québec • Bath, United Kingdom

Place a photo here.

Fill
cho

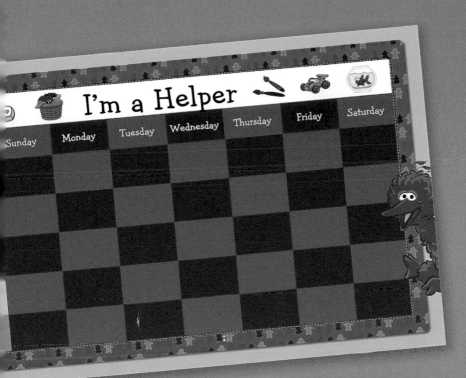

Do you like helping? Elmo does! Elmo likes to help his mommy set the table for dinner, his daddy rake the leaves, and his teacher water the plants in his classroom!

Elmo also helps by learning to take care of himself—by dressing himself, brushing his teeth, or washing his hands.

Elmo sometimes needs help to remember to do these things. But he has a special "I'm a Helper" chart to remind him! Every time he helps out, he puts a sticker on his chart.

Let's look at all the ways Elmo and his friends help out!

Good morning, Elmo!
After he wakes up, Elmo straightens the blankets on his bed and puts his pajamas in the laundry basket. Sometimes he pretends he is playing basketball and tosses his jammies into the basket from across the room. Score!

Elmo is also learning how to dress himself. But sometimes Elmo needs to ask for help to put his shirt on correctly. Practice makes perfect, Elmo!

What clothes can you put on all by yourself?

Elmo is learning that another way to help is to practice healthy habits! First thing every morning he brushes his teeth and washes his face. Elmo also remembers to use the potty.

He always tells his mommy when he needs to go. He uses the potty, wipes with toilet paper, flushes the toilet, then carefully washes his hands with water and soap. This keeps germs away.

soap

Make sure you use soap and water when you wash your hands.

Bert and Ernie like to have their friends come to their house to play. Playing is fun, but usually there is a mess to clean up afterwards, so Ernie and Elmo pick up toys and put them in the toy box.

Bert helps by putting the books back on the shelf. Great job, guys!

How many green books are on the bookshelf?

Pets are so much fun, but they need lots of care.
Taking good care of a pet is a great way to help out!
Elmo's pet fish, Dorothy, needs her special fish food.
Elmo helps by feeding her every day!

Grover's kitty needs food, water, and lots of
cuddles. Grover also brushes her fur. This makes
her purr!

Dogs need food, water, and lots of exercise.
Murray walks his neighbor's dog every day.
It's fun for both of them!

What is your pet's name? If you don't have
a pet, what kind would you like?

It's Community Clean-up Day! Everyone on Sesame Street has come out to help. Big Bird is cleaning his nest. Oscar is picking up trash. Bert and Ernie get to work sweeping the sidewalk while Murray waters the flowers.

When two or more people work together, it's called cooperation!

The community garden is another place Elmo's friends can help out. Elmo's favorite job is planting seeds in the soft dirt. Abby and the Twiddlebugs are great at pulling out the weeds so more vegetables and flowers can grow.

What would you plant if you had a garden?

Grover stops by to pitch in. Big Bird helps
by hanging a bird feeder in the tree!

School is a great place to help out! Monsters are busy all day long, but before everyone goes home, it's chore time! Each student has a job to do to make the classroom ready for the next day—and to help their teacher.

Prairie Dawn erases the blackboard. Elmo feeds
the class fish and Rosita puts all the books in the
bookcase. Zoe's favorite chore is cleaning the
paintbrushes!

What other chores need
to be done at school?

The supermarket is busy today! Elmo is helping his daddy find all the fruits and vegetables on his list.

Rosita is busy helping her daddy, too! She can reach things that he can't from his wheelchair.

What are your favorite fruits and vegetables?

When the shopping is done, Rosita helps her daddy carry the groceries home. You are a good helper, Rosita!

Elmo's mommy loves to cook. Today she is making cupcakes with Elmo and his friends! She has given everyone a job to do.

How do you help in the kitchen?
What is your favorite food
to help cook?

Abby stirs the batter, the Count helps measure
ingredients, and Elmo decorates the cupcakes
after they come out of the oven and have cooled.
Of course someone must EAT the cupcakes!

That's a job for Cookie Monster!

Setting the table is one of Zoe's favorite ways to help. She uses this picture to help her remember where to put the plate, napkin, fork, spoon, and cup. Zoe knows to let a grown-up put the knife in place!

She always remembers to wash her hands before setting the table—and also before eating!

Zoe loves to have her friends come over for
dinner. They each know that part of being a good
guest means helping to clean up. Zoe and her friends
help clear the table. After Zoe's mom washes the
dishes, Elmo and Big Bird help by putting them away.

When everyone helps, the cleaning is done in no time! Zoe's mommy thanks everyone for being such wonderful helpers.

How do you help out in the kitchen?

At the end of the day, Elmo helps to get himself ready for bed. He uses the potty, then takes a warm bath. He makes sure he washes all his body parts— arms, legs, back, feet, and especially his face!

Elmo puts on clean pajamas and then brushes his teeth. Now he's almost ready for his bedtime story and good-night kisses! But, he has one last thing to do.

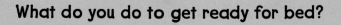

What do you do to get ready for bed?

Elmo needs to put the last sticker on his "I'm a Helper" chart for the day. Today his chart is full of stickers—one for each time that Elmo helped someone! Elmo is a super helper—and so are all his Sesame Street friends!
How do you help?

Place a photo here.

I'm a Helper

Fill in chores	Sunday	Monday	Tuesday	Wednesday	Thursday	Friday	Saturday
Brush Teeth							
Feed Dorothy							
r s							
able							
ash							